# The Secrets of Herbs

## Herbs and Spices

*Rita Schnitzer*

*Illustrations by Rosa Batlle*

Peter Zozulak
London VICTORIA
2006 MARCH

ORBIS · LONDON

*Also published in the same series*
**The Mystery of Perfume**

© 1984 by Ediciones Elfos, Barcelona
First published in Great Britain by Orbis Publishing
Limited, London 1985

Printed in Spain
ISBN 0–85613–874–6

The Publishers have taken every care to ensure the
accuracy of the information in this book but disclaim any
responsibility for the medical application of the herbs and
spices described.

Little by little, man has gone about discovering many of the secrets of plants.

When salt was first added to food in prehistoric times, thus making the mere need for food a small pleasure, this represented the first step toward culinary art. Ancient cultures achieved remarkable knowledge in the use of herbs and mastered the art of seasoning dishes and making remedies and perfumes to enhance the seductive skills of women. Sappho, the beautiful poetess of ancient Greece, spread marjoram in her hair and rubbed her body with mint and thyme.

Although much of this knowledge was lost in the early Middle Ages, the Benedictine monks began to recover it.

In contemporary times the powerful competition of man-made products has overridden interest in natural substances and in many cases they have been forgotten. But having tired of his artificial life, man has been invaded by a yearning for paradise lost and once again has placed his trust in Nature.

When we find ourselves swathed in the fragrance of plants, don't we want to know their names, their features, their secrets? This book will help you discover the treasure Nature offers us for our health, joy, pleasure and . . . our naturalness.

This aromatic herb, similar to wild fennel and green anise, was known in the ancient world. The Roman gladiators rubbed their bodies with the essential oil from its seeds to fortify themselves before combat. And lactating mothers steeped its seeds in water and rubbed it on their breasts to make their babies go to sleep after nursing.

Dill arrived in Europe from Persia, its country of origin, thanks to the monks who cultivated it in their monastery gardens to use as a cooking and medicinal herb. The plant grows wild in the countryside and prefers dry sunny soils. Its tiny yellow flowers come out in summer and bees are attracted to its nectar.

The finely chopped fresh leaves are used in salads, soups and sauces for fish. They are added at the end and not cooked, to preserve all their properties and flavour. The dried seeds are used in pickling sauces and marinades, especially for pickles and onions.

The fruit is harvested at the end of summer when it is fully ripened and turns brown, to be spread out on trays and dried in an airy room.

The properties of the dill plant are similar to those of anise and fennel. Taken as an infusion it cures diseases of the mouth and eliminates gases, hiccups and vomiting. Chewing a few seeds purifies the breath, but chewing too many may make you fall asleep in your lover's arms.

### Infusion

Pour boiling water into a cup with a pinch of dill. Cover and steep for five to ten minutes, then filter and drink hot. You can drink up to three cups a day.

Originating in southern Russia, chervil arrived in Greece some 200 years before Christ. Later on it was spread to many European countries by Roman expeditions. The Latin word *cerefolium* means 'Cere's leaf' because the herb was used in banquets in honour of Ceres, goddess of the land and vegetation.

In Europe chervil is cultivated in gardens and sometimes grows wild. It should not be confused with hemlock, which is poisonous and, among other feats, removed Socrates from this world.

Chervil is a refined seasoning prized by every gastronome worthy of the name. Its finely chopped leaves season salads, omelettes, stews, vegetables, spaghetti dishes, fish and lamb. They are added fresh at the last minute and not boiled.

The best way to preserve the leaves is by freezing since drying causes the herb's delightful flavour to disappear.

The leaves are refreshing, cleansing and diuretic, but should not be used by breast-feeding women because they block milk secretion.

A herbal tea made with chervil is indicated for some heart conditions, bronchitis and gout. It can be used also in compresses to relieve eyes swollen from cold, wind, sun, tears and 'too much the night before'.

**Ninon de Lenclos's beauty recipe**
To prevent wrinkles, boil chervil leaves (a handful for 1 litre of water) and use the water to wash your face every day.

This is a remedy recommended by the famous Ninon de Lenclos who, at the age of eighty, still roused passionate desires in her admirers.

The Romans hid sprigs of tarragon under their tunics to protect themselves from snake bites; this belief is reflected in the Latin name. The tarragon, or 'little dragon', plant has twisting, winding roots and is said to look like the dragon that killed Hippolytus, Theseus's son.

There are two forms of tarragon: the Russian variety (*Artemesia dracunculoides*), more robust but less aromatic, and the French type, with its spicier flavour. The latter is more commonly used.

Because of its noble aroma and fine but penetrating flavour, tarragon is highly prized as an aromatic herb. Another definite point in its favour is that it does not produce acid. In French cuisine it belongs to the famous *fines herbes*, the classic herbs of refined cooking.

The leaves are best cut off at the end of summer and can be frozen, although it is better to use them fresh. They are delicious in salads, soups, omelettes, pickles, herb vinegar and a wide variety of sauces.

Tarragon is not very well known in its therapeutic attributes, but its use as a substitute for pepper, salt and vinegar makes it a simple and effective remedy for obese persons and those who suffer from heart disease. When used as a seasoning it stimulates the appetite and facilitates digestion.

**Tarragon vinegar**

Drop a few sprigs of fresh herb, picked before flowering, into a jar and add white wine vinegar. Keep the mixture in a warm, well-lit place for two weeks.

The mugwort plant signifies happiness in the language of flowers and owes its name to the Greek goddess Artemis, who gave aid to women in illness. The Romans put mugwort leaves in their sandals to keep their feet from hurting when they had to walk long distances. In those times magic properties were attributed to the plant, as evidenced by the numerous popular names given it. The Germanic peoples wore wreaths and belts made of mugwort on St John's Eve – in some places it is also known as St John's herb – while they danced around the sacred fire. When the ceremony was over, they threw the magic plant into the fire to burn up symbolically all the evil omens. In the Middle Ages witches used mugwort to drive away demons.

Indigenous to southern Europe, mugwort grows in many parts of the world. It gives off a discreet odour and the leaves contain absinthe, making them too bitter to be used in marinades. Only the buds can be used and they are harvested before opening in summer and are good for seasoning fatty dishes like goose, duck and pork by adding just a pinch at the start of cooking.

Mugwort is also used in making liqueurs.

The roots have tonic and stimulant properties and are indicated for convulsions in babies. The leaves, taken in the form of an infusion, activate digestion and regulate menstruation.

**Massage oil**
Place as many mugwort leaves as will fit in a bottle of almond oil and leave it in the sun for four weeks, shaking the bottle now and then. The resulting oil is excellent for massaging tired, swollen feet.

This plant, which is completely covered with fine down, takes its name from the Latin *borra*, meaning hair. Borage, wrote a famous herbalist in the sixteenth century, 'makes men and women happy and gay, taking away all sadness and melancholy . . . and calms the restless and lunatic.'

Originating in the Orient, this plant has become widely popular. It is commonly cultivated and grows wild as well in abandoned fields and along the edges of roads. Its bright blue flowers come out like stars at the end of winter and last all summer, and are a great attraction for bees.

The young leaves and flowers – but not whole sprigs – are harvested in summer, preferably when just starting to flower. They must be used freshly cut because they do not keep well. The leaves, very finely chopped because of the down, are delicious in salads – especially when combined with parsley and fennel – and in cold sauces, soups and beverages. They impart a spicy flavour similar to cucumber and produce a feeling of euphoria. In many regions the leaves are cooked like spinach and can also be rolled in egg and flour to make a kind of fritters. The flowers are also eaten and used as sprightly adornments in soups and salads. A bunch of flowers combined with fennel and basil makes a decorative centrepiece for a table.

In popular medicine, borage is appreciated for its gentleness. The flowers induce perspiration and the leaves are diuretic and indicated for treating rheumatism. An infusion of borage relieves colds and bronchitis and fortifies persons who suffer from heart disease of nervous origin.

Capers come from the Middle East and the Mediterranean and were well known in antiquity. We find them in the dry areas in the south of the Iberian peninsula and the Balearic Islands where they cover rocks and old walls with their lovely, showy flowers with large white or pink petals.

The unopened buds are harvested at the beginning of summer and used for flavouring vinegar, marinades and sauces for fish. To preserve capers put them in a large, wide-mouth bottle and cover them with good-quality vinegar and a little salt. Cover tightly and keep in a cool place, changing the vinegar now and then. Crushed with parsley and a little mustard, they can be mixed with mayonnaise to give it an exquisite flavour. Small capers are the most aromatic and appreciated as a spicy appetizer, together with olives and onions. They are a good stimulant for the stomach – as long as you don't overdo it! As the old saying from Castile goes: 'Eating capers after curds will send you straight to the grave.'

Capers are not commonly used in medicine although the buds and roots are considered effective as a diuretic and for cases of arteriosclerosis.

**Caper sauce**
Melt 50g of butter in a saucepan, add 1 tablespoon flour and stir with a wooden spoon to keep lumps from forming. Dilute with 3 tablespoons of stock and continue stirring about 10 minutes more until the sauce thickens slightly. Remove the pan from the stove and add an egg yolk and finely chopped capers.

This is a plant from the New World that was unknown to the ancient cultures of the Mediterranean. The pepper plant arrived in Spain thanks to Christopher Columbus and spread throughout the country; today it is cultivated to be eaten whole or used for seasoning in tropical and temperate countries.

The whole fruit is harvested fully ripened in summer and dried in the sun. It can be powdered and used like paprika for red colouring and is rich in vitamins, especially vitamin C. The fruit contains capsaicin, a strong substance that irritates the skin and mucose membranes and causes a burning sensation.

Peppers are used for making salads, various soups and as an accompaniment to meat. In small amounts they stimulate the appetite and activate gastric secretions; eaten in excess they may produce inflammation in the stomach and intestinal lesions.

There are many varieties of sweeter peppers – both red and green – that are low in capsaicin and these can be prepared as appetizing vegetable dishes.

It is believed that a mixture of pepper and gentian, without sugar, makes a good remedy for an overly enthusiastic drinking spree.

The tincture is used to keep hair from falling out and the pharmaceutical industry uses it to make ointments to relieve the pains of rheumatism and arthritis.

### Recommendation
Don't let peppers come into contact with boiling oil as they will turn black and become inedible because of their high sugar content.

Cinnamon is one of the oldest of all spices, and it was the Phoenicians who took it from India, its country of origin, to Egypt. In Biblical times it was considered the symbol of wisdom and served to perfume the tunics of royal couples, although such noble use did not keep the Hebrews from using it to combat fevers. Nero burned more cinnamon at the funeral of the Empress Poppaea than was produced in an entire year in Arabia.

Always green and fragrant, cinnamon will not grow in Europe. It is cultivated in India and Brazil for its bark which, freed of the green layer that covers it, cut in strips and dried, is used by cooks and pastry makers for its peculiar aroma that imparts a refined flavour to a wide variety of foods.

Chinese cinnamon bark (*Cinnamomum cassia*) is thicker, darker and of poorer quality than that of Indian cinnamon.

Cinnamon is used in curry sauces, soups, stews, apple compote, and in pastry making it is an ingredient in creams, custards, crêpes, tarts, ice cream and in punch. It is also used for making perfumes.

As a medicinal plant, cinnamon is added to elixirs and other preparations as an aid against gases, flu and weakness. It also helps to regulate menstruation and is considered an aphrodisiac.

**Elixir**
Place 25g of cinnamon bark and 10g of fresh mint leaves in 1 litre of good-quality sweet wine for two days and then filter. Drink a small amount whenever you feel weak.

For the ancients this beautiful, gently fragrant flower was of real worth. In Egypt the gardens of Luxor were heavily planted with it and in Greece the herb was the inspiration of many legends. One of them relates how the young Crocus, because of his unfortunate love for the nymph Smilax, was changed into saffron and she in turn became the plant that bears her name (sarsaparilla).

The plant is not native to the Mediterranean but came from the Middle East. The name of saffron comes from the Arabic word *sahafarn*, meaning thread, because of its thread-shaped stigmas. Saffron came to Europe through Andalusia, brought there by the Arabs in the ninth century, and was an ingredient in numerous dishes in the Middle Ages. Henry VIII of England was so fond of it as a seasoning that he forbade the ladies of the court to use it for dyeing their hair.

The flowers are harvested in early autumn and the bright orange stigmas pressed under heavy boards to form a solid mass. Some 14,000 flowers are needed to obtain 100g of saffron. Because of the costly cultivation, harvesting and drying processes required to prepare it, saffron has always been an expensive delicacy. In the Middle Ages, counterfeiters of this herb were burned or buried alive.

In the Mediterranean countries saffron is commonly used as a seasoning. Its pigment is so strong that two stigmas are enough to colour three litres of water. Spanish saffron is considered the best.

Saffron is not commonly used in medicine because of its high cost, although it has properties that make it good for treating bronchitis and coughs. Saffron is a stimulant and is considered an aphrodisiac. Taken in excess it can cause heavy bleeding.

Ancient cultures were familiar with this aromatic plant, which was one of the four 'fiery seeds' – the others were fennel, dill and caraway. The Egyptians used it in stews with pepper and placed its seeds, along with other foods, in the pharaohs' tombs. For the Greeks cumin was the symbol of greed because of its tiny fruit while for the Romans it was an absolute essential at festivals as the personification of the god Crepitus because of its sedative properties. In the Middle Ages cumin was an aristocratic spice and was used especially for seasoning poultry. In the north of Germany it was the custom to wear a bag of cumin around the neck for protection from witches.

Native to Turkestan, cumin was brought to Europe by the Arabs and is found growing wild in some parts of the Mediterranean. Its white or pink flowers come out in June and the fruit matures in summer.

Cumin seed is commonly used to season all types of sauces and stews, especially those to accompany meat. It is also an ingredient in curry powders, marinades and Indian hot sauces. Because it facilitates digestion, it is recommended to go with pulses and cabbage, but it does not mix well with other seasonings. The Dutch use cumin for flavouring cheese and the Germans have preserved the oriental tradition of putting it in bread. Pastries, sausages and sauerkraut are all the better for its perky flavour.

As a medicinal plant it has the same properties as anise, although it is somewhat less effective, and is used in the form of an infusion, as a powder and tincture.

The clove tree, which grows to a height of twenty metres, originated in India and was imported by the Chinese 400 years before Christ, who gave it the poetic name of *Ki-she-Kiang* – bird's tongue. The women of the court used it to perfume their breath when they were to appear before the emperor. Marco Polo was the first European to see a clove and it made its appearance in Europe in the eleventh century, where it was considered a rare spice and an item of luxury. All cloves consumed in the world came from the Molucca Islands until in the eighteenth century a group of Frenchmen risked their lives to steal a few seeds. Thus cloves came to be cultivated on the island of Mauritius and from there spread to most of the other tropical countries.

The closed buds of the reddish-purple flowers are shaped like nails – thus the origin of the name, from the Latin word for nail. They are hand harvested between August and November and left to dry in the sun, where they turn brown. A tree begins to produce when it is six years old and continues until it is a hundred. Cloves are used whole or crushed for flavouring meat, fish, sauces and vegetables. Sometimes they are stuck whole in an onion to aid the spread of their aroma. They stimulate the appetite, facilitate digestion and are a good antiseptic. Cloves give flavour to pastry products, liqueurs and punch and perfume to cosmetics, and essence of clove is used for dental caries and toothaches.

**Painkiller and dentrifrice**
Place two cloves in a cup and pour boiling water over them. The warm liquid is used as a mouth rinse to ease the pain of toothaches and is also effective as a mouthwash for bad breath.

In ancient times fennel was appreciated as a medicinal herb and seasoning. The Romans called it *foeniculum* because of its odour like dry hay. In the Dionysian mysteries the participants adorned themselves with wreaths of fennel because, in the language of flowers, fennel meant strength.

Throughout the centuries the plant was brought to our part of the world from Asia. This elegant plant with its aromatic perfume and bitter flavour grows in dry, sunny soils. Its tiny yellow flowers appear in summer and are the delight of bees.

The mature fruit can be collected several times a year because it does not all ripen at the same time. It is picked when it has turned brown, dried and pounded to remove the seeds.

Fennel is used in cooking, pastry making, cosmetics and medicine. Fresh or dried leaves are good in sauces for fish, with cabbage and vegetable soups, for seasoning pork, and in pickles and stewed apple. The cultivated sweet variety makes a delicious aromatic vegetable dish with a slightly sugary, anise-like flavour. It can also be eaten raw in salad. An infusion made with fennel seeds relieves gases, is indicated for asthma, coughs, influenza, colic and menstrual discomfort, stimulates milk secretion in nursing mothers and plays an important role in pediatrics. Our grandmothers recommended an infusion of fennel for easing difficult digestion in babies, especially when weaning. Young mothers would be glad to learn that this home remedy can spare them and their babies many sleepless nights. The infusion can also be used for washing swollen eyes.

Bay enjoyed considerable prestige among the ancients and was one of the favourite plants of the gods. It was sacred to Apollo and the priestesses chewed its leaves to enhance their prophetic talents. Roman generals wrapped their victory messages in bay leaves, and heroes and poets were crowned with bay leaves to symbolize glory, victory and peace. The Latin name of the plant comes from *laudare*, meaning to praise, and it was also said to have magical and medical properties: it kept misfortune away and cured contagious diseases. This is why Aesculapius, god of medicine, is always shown with bay leaves. During the Renaissance students were adorned with bay leaves and berries when they had passed their examinations – the *bacca-laureati* – a custom brought to mind today in our words 'baccalaureate' and 'bachelor'.

The bay plant, with its glossy green leaves, grows wild around the Mediterranean and embellishes gardens as an ornamental bush. Rubbing the leaves releases a balsamic fragrance, and they are also used as part of a *bouquet garni* in cooking.

Leaves are picked in autumn and, dried or fresh, lend their pleasant fragrance to numerous popular dishes in Mediterranean cuisine – soups, vegetables, sauces, fish and meat.

In addition to their culinary value, bay leaves have medicinal properties. They are stimulating and antiseptic. Baths perfumed with bay leaves are relaxing. An infusion made with the fruit and leaves stimulates digestion and relieves coughing. An essence is extracted from the black berries, harvested when ripe in summer and dried, that is used in pharmacy to prepare medications for rheumatism; the same essence is also used in cosmetics.

*Lavandula spica* Lavender

This is one of the most popular of all perfumed plants. Its name means 'to wash' since the Romans took lavender baths and rubbed themselves down with it to cure skin diseases.

Lavender is native to southern Europe and grows wild in the Mediterranean countries in dry rocky, sunny places. The entire plant gives off a delightful fragrance that attracts bees and butterflies. The flowers, that open in spring and autumn, are blue–violet or somewhat paler and may even be white, depending on the variety. Lavender is cultivated as an ornamental plant in gardens and in large fields, especially in southern France, for the perfume industry.

There are many ways to use lavender: as an infusion, essence, powder, in the bath and in inhalations for laryngitis, coughs, asthma, rheumatism, bronchitis, fatigue, stomach ailments and insomnia. A lavender bath relieves nervous excitation. For centuries housewives have used lavender as an insecticide. It perfumes closets and keeps moths away. It is seldom used in cooking although it can be added in small amounts to poultry dishes.

**Lavender water**
Combine the following ingredients and keep for 20 days: 200g 80° alcohol, 10g essence of lavender and 1g cinnamon. Filter and keep the liquid in a bottle.

Lemon balm has been popular from the time of the ancient Greeks. The Arabs, who brought the plant from the Orient to Spain, considered it excellent for strengthening the heart and the brain and Paracelsus, the famous German-Swiss physician, praised it saying that 'lemon balm, of all that is produced by the earth, is the best plant for the heart.' In the seventeenth century the French barefoot Carmelites invented the recipe for the still well-known 'Carmen water' that is widely used as a tranquillizer, anti-spasmodic and for hysteria.

The plant grows wild and is cultivated in cool, moist soil. When rubbed between the fingers, the plant gives off a pleasant lemon scent. Its pinkish white flowers are a delight for bees; hence its Latin name which, translated from Greek, means 'honey flower'.

In cooking the flowered tips and fresh or dried leaves are added at the last minute, without boiling, to give a lemon flavour to dishes and to drinks. Lemon balm is also used in making liqueurs and perfumes.

As a medicinal plant it is used in the form of infusion, tincture, medicinal wine and as a drink to calm the nerves, pain and digestive ailments.

**Carmen water**
This French recipe is made by combining 2.5 litres 80° alcohol, 350g fresh lemon balm flowers, 75g orange or lemon rind, 40g nutmeg, 40g cloves, 40g whole cinnamon and 20g coriander. After 4 days filter and keep the liquid in a bottle. The usual dose is half a teaspoon in a cup of hot sugared water, or poured over a cube of sugar and dissolved slowly in the mouth.

According to Greek legend, Mintha, daughter of a river, was a concubine of Hades, lord of the Underworld. His legitimate wife, Persephone, in a jealous rage changed her into a plant and condemned her to sterility. It is said that this is why the fruit of the mint plant is misshapen and it grows in damp soil near water. In antiquity mint plants were braided into wreaths and used at festivals and ceremonies, in addition to its use as a home remedy. Today it makes a favourite herbal tea and is considered to have aphrodisiac properties.

Mint comes from the Far East and has been known in Europe for the past three centuries. Its tiny flowers are purple, pink or white, depending on which of the many varieties they belong to, and they bloom in summer.

The leaves are harvested just before the plant blossoms, when their menthol concentration is highest.

They are used fresh or dried for salads, soups, vegetables, omelettes, pulses, sauces and meats, especially in summer because they freshen the mouth and purify the breath. Mint should not be combined with other seasonings. A few finely chopped mint leaves rubbed across the forehead and temples will relieve a headache. The herbal tea is effective against intoxication, difficult digestion, dizziness, nervousness, migraine and insomnia. But it is harmful to the nervous system when taken in large doses. The menthol is used to prepare syrups, dentifrices, sweets and liqueurs.

**Mint liqueur**

Place 50g of dried mint leaves in 600cc of 60° alcohol and leave the mixture for a week. To this add 165cc of boiled water with 335g of sugar, after cooling. Filter and bottle.

Native to the Molucca Islands in Indonesia, nutmeg was the last Asian spice to arrive in Europe in the twelfth century, where it was first known as 'Indian nut'. Its name derives from a preparation called *suffumis gum moschatum*, and the famous medical school at Salerno considered it healthy when taken in moderation and dangerous – even fatal – when taken in large doses.

The tree, with its delicately scented evergreen leaves, is cultivated today in tropical regions. The tiny flowers become the fruit that gives two spices: nutmeg and mace. The nutmeg is the hard kernel of the fruit with the outer layer removed, and the fleshy covering of the kernel is the mace. One female tree will produce some 2000 nuts; it blossoms and the fruit ripens throughout the year. After the nuts are harvested they are treated with lime to sterilize them and protect them from insects.

Mace is used to flavour stews and in sausages while nutmeg, with its strong aroma and warm, tart flavour, is ground and added to cabbage, beans, mashed potatoes, cheese soufflés, fruit salad, custard, punch and liqueurs. Only very small amounts are used; even half a kernel taken quickly can have a narcotic effect and cause convulsions.

Nutmeg has an exciting effect and facilitates digestion. Nutmeg butter, obtained by squeezing the fruit hot, is used in ointments for relieving rheumatic pain.

**Suggestion**
To prevent motion sickness, take one egg yolk beaten with nutmeg.

The Romans called water cress *nasi tortium* because of its peppery effect, and they used it dried and ground as a sneezing powder. It was one of the favourite foods of the ancient Persians who ate bread seasoned with cress when they went hunting.

Water cress is found nearly all over the world in temperate zones and in clear, slow-moving fresh water. Its pungent taste, similar to mustard and radish, makes it a universally appreciated seasoning. Because it is rich in vitamins A, C, D and E and iodine, phosphorus and iron, it is a good addition to salads or a garnish with roast meats. It is so rich in iron that the leaves and stems turn dark if exposed to the air for too long before being eaten. It is best to use water cress fresh since cooking and drying destroy many of its curative properties.

When gathering water cress, make sure it is growing in unpolluted water because it may be a vehicle for typhoid fever. It must be carefully washed and eaten in small amounts since it may cause stomach irritation. It may also have abortive properties.

The plant is an excellent diuretic and laxative if taken as a juice or cold infusion.

The famous naturopath Maurice Mességué recommended poultices made with beaten egg white mixed with water cress to relieve the pains of arthritis.

**Eggs with water cress**
Cut a few hard-boiled eggs in half. Mix the yolks with a little oil and finely chopped water cress and return the mixture to the cut whites. Serve with green salad and whole-grain bread.

Basil comes from India and was considered a royal plant. For the Hindus it was, and still is, a sacred plant, dedicated to the gods Krishna and Vishnu. In Egypt it was used in offerings to the gods and used in preparing balms. It played an important role in popular Greek and Roman traditions in which it was considered to have magical properties and was of both funeral and erotic significance. This aromatic plant owes its botanical name to the extraordinary scent it emanates, worthy of kings (in Greek *ozein*: to smell; *basileus*: king). Basil held a place of honour among the culinary herbs, until it was dethroned by the invasion of oriental spices. Like so many other aromatic plants, it attracted renewed interest during the Second World War, when spices were scarce in Europe.

Basil is grown in temperate countries. Planted in flower pots, it brightens up windows and balconies. In cold areas it must be kept indoors because it is easily affected by frost.

The pungent, aromatic flavour of the leaves is especially good when combined with tomato in sauces or salads. It can also be used in soups, vegetables, pizzas and roast meats. The ground leaves mixed with garlic are the basis for Italian *pesto*. To preserve the leaves the stems should be cut in summer when the white flowers appear.

As a home remedy, an infusion made with the leaves and flowers is relaxing and relieves headaches, colds, coughs, intestinal ailments, colic, bad breath and weakness in general.

**Suggestion**
A pot of basil in the room keeps flies away.

*Origanum vulgaris*  # Oregano

The name of this plant comes from the Greek words *oros* and *ganos*, mountain adornment. Ever since remote times oregano has been known as a seasoning and medicinal plant. In the Middle Ages it was grown in monastery gardens because it was thought to have powers to protect people from the devil.

In Southern Europe wild oregano lives on sunny, rocky hills and in abandoned fields. Its mauve flowers give off a delightful unmistakable odour and are an attraction for bees.

The entire plant is harvested when it blossoms, from July to September. The heaviest stems are cut off and the plants are dried in bunches hung in the shade and kept in glass jars.

The flowering tips are used fresh and dried as seasoning for meat, stuffing, dishes with eggplant and zucchini and for marinating olives. Oregano gives off its full flavour especially in pizzas or in combination with tomato and melted cheese. Today the plant is a typical herb in Italian cuisine but is also universally appreciated.

An infusion of oregano facilitates digestion, relieves coughing and asthma and is used as a gargle for sore throats. The fresh leaves can be chopped and heated in a pan and applied on parts of the body affected by rheumatism and stiffness to relieve pain.

**Oregano bath**
Boil three handfuls of dried flowered tips for a few minutes in two litres of water. Leave to stand for half an hour, filter and add to bath water. It is an excellent remedy for fatigue, muscle pain and rheumatism.

## Petroselinum crispum *Parsley*

This plant derives its botanical name from *petra*, meaning rock, as in its wild state it is commonly found among rocks and around walls. For the Greeks parsley was a sacred plant that signified joy and festivities. It was also the symbol of death and resurrection, birth and triumph, and the Greeks and Romans adorned the tombs of their dead with parsley wreaths. The *Iliad* tells how the magic isle of the nymph Calypso was covered with a carpet of parsley. The plant was thought to be an aphrodisiac and the nymph seduced Ulysses and kept him with her for years. In the Middle Ages parsley began to be used for its aromatic qualities, thanks to Charlemagne who ordered this plant and many others to be grown in his gardens.

Because of its refined aroma and discreet flavour, parsley has become the most commonly used seasoning in the world. The roots and leaves are best used fresh and the dried seeds add a pleasant taste to cheese.

Parsley is harvested before it flowers in June, when its properties are at their best. It is the richest source of vitamin A and iron and also has vitamin C, calcium and manganese, making it a valuable contribution to good health, especially in children because of its growth-promoting properties.

As a home remedy it acts as a stimulant, diuretic, aids digestion and is effective against diseases of the intestine, kidneys and liver and menstrual discomfort. Chewing a sprig after eating garlic will eliminate bad breath. Taken in large doses it is an aphrodisiac, but can also be poisonous and cause miscarriage. It is a fatal poison for parrots.

Anise comes from the Near East and is mentioned in an Egyptian papyrus of 1500 B.C. For the Chinese it was a sacred plant; they burned its leaves at funerals and used its seeds to flavour wedding dishes. In antiquity anise was used as a remedy for snake bites. It was brought to Europe by the Benedictines in Charlemagne's time and was used during the Middle Ages to season bread – as the Romans had used it before. It also served as a tranquilliser for attacks of hysteria and to relieve the pains of childbirth.

The anise plant is rarely found in the wild; it is grown in many countries for its seeds. Its tiny white flowers are similar to fennel but their perfume is more delicate.

The aromatic fruit is harvested in summer when it is dry and mature, and shelled to remove the seeds.

Anise is one of the herbs most commonly used in our cuisine and medicine. It perks up sauces, soups, red cabbage, tender carrots and curried peas, is used in pastry and is especially prized for flavouring liqueurs. As a home remedy the seeds are steeped in water and drunk to expel gases, to relieve coughing, bronchitis and asthma and to aid sleep and stimulate milk secretion.

### Anise liqueur
Place 250g of fine sugar in a container with 375cc of water and leave for a few hours. When the syrupy liquid is ready, mix it with half a litre of 90° alcohol, 2 drops of essence of anise, 1 drop of essence of cinnamon and half a teaspoon of cinnamon. Mix well and pour into a bottle. A small glass after meals makes an excellent digestive.

## *Piper nigrum* **Black Pepper**

Black pepper is a universal spice, held in high esteem by the ancient Greeks and introduced into the Mediterranean countries by Alexander the Great, like so many other spices. It was so sought after that wars broke out over it.

Black pepper and its white cousin come from the same plant, which originated in eastern India and is now cultivated in nearly all tropical countries. Black pepper is obtained from the unripened fruit and white pepper, with its gentler flavour and odour, from the ripe fruit. If the unripened fruit is put in vinegar or salt water, the result is green pepper, which is commonly used as a spicy seasoning for steaks, herb sauces and fowl; white pepper is good for 'white' meats – fish and fowl – and white sauce, while black pepper is best for red meat.

The flowers form red berries after their third year and can be harvested for about fifteen years. Indigenous peoples use the old roots to make a refreshing drink.

Pepper unfolds its aroma best if it is kept in grains and ground just before using it; this also helps preserve its properties. A small amout of pepper facilitates digestion but its prolonged use may be harmful, especially in persons who suffer from liver disorders, inflammations of the bowel and haemorrhoids.

For use around the home, mixing a few grains of black pepper with naphthalene and camphor makes a most effective mothball.

### Steak tartare
Mix equal amounts of capers, onion and green pepper to season a steak tartare (raw ground meat). The refined aroma of the green pepper makes this dish a most appetizing mouthful.

The name 'rosemary' means sea spray, an apt description of this blue-flowered Mediterranean plant. It is a herb with a long history of use in the region and one that held a place of honour in antiquity. It was sacred to Venus and it was believed that it gave eternal youth. The Romans saw in this evergreen-leaf plant the symbol of memory and fidelity, and brides carried it in their wedding bouquets. The Greeks used this 'flower of Olympus' as incense and students sought it because it was said to improve the memory. It is also said that Queen Elizabeth of Hungary, old and ill, recovered her health and was rejuvenated by rosemary. Her elixir is easily prepared by mixing essence of rosemary with lavender, mint and penny-royal.

Rosemary blooms nearly all year round and is a constant attraction for bees; the honey made from its nectar has a distinctive flavour.

The tiny leaves and young sprouts are excellent for seasoning; they should be added at the end of cooking to keep the essential oil from evaporating. As well as imparting a delicious flavour to dishes, this herb aids and stimulates digestion.

An old refrain says that 'one could write a book on the virtues of rosemary'. When used to make an infusion or aromatic wine, it relieves difficult digestive problems and menstrual pain but – be careful! If taken in excess it is said to cause miscarriages and to thin the blood. It is also said to cure impotence and frigidity. Rosemary baths are stimulating and fortifying. Breathing the fumes from a handful of dried leaves on a hot grill will cure a cold. And rosemary is also used to make cologne, soap and shampoo that prevents loss of hair.

In some countries sorrel is known as the 'vinegar plant' because of the acidity of its leaves. This attractive pink-flowered plant was esteemed by the ancient Egyptians and Romans for its laxative and culinary properties. It was popular in the Middle Ages and was to be found in any garden of aromatic herbs.

Sorrel is common all over Europe and grows in damp soil, in forests, meadows and along the edges of roads.

Its fresh leaves and stems are used in salads, vegetable soups, green sauces, scrambled eggs, seafood dishes, and stuffings for fowl and game, and can also be eaten like a vegetable together with spinach. But it can be a dangerous plant and must be treated with some care because the acid in its leaves can cause serious harm, and should not be eaten by persons who suffer from heart or kidney disease, gout or rheumatism. It is recommended as a balm for numerous skin diseases and when taken in the form of an infusion or juice is a good laxative and diuretic. It is also rich in vitamin C. French sorrel, *R. scutatus*, is the variety most appreciated because it is less acid.

## Sorrel purée
Boil fresh leaves for 15 minutes, chop finely and stew in butter. Cooked in this way, sorrel is delicious with meat, fish or omelettes.

Sage takes it name from the Latin words *salvus*, healthy, and *officina*, pharmacy. Ever since remote times it has been said that the plant gives long life. The Egyptians were familiar with the therapeutic qualities of this plant and, following epidemics of the plague, they made the women drink its juice to make them fertile again. The Greeks dedicated sage to Zeus, their supreme god. The beautiful women of the time rubbed their teeth with a sage leaf to make them whiter and shinier. In the Middle Ages the plant also occupied a place of honour among medicinal herbs.

Sage grows typically in the dry, sunny regions around the Mediterranean. The entire plant gives off a strong, pleasant aroma and its purple flowers, that come out in summer, are frequented by bees. The leaves and flowers are harvested just before the blossoms open.

Fresh or dried leaves are used to flavour fish, meat, vegetables and sweets. They are also good for protecting clothing from moths, preserving beauty and keeping healthy. To purify the breath chew a single fresh leaf for a long time. An infusion of sage is said to relieve menstrual pains and stomach-ache, and to help those suffering from liver and kidney stones, diabetes, asthma, coughs and cold sweats. Gargling with a sage infusion relieves a sore throat. The herb should not be taken in excess as it may cause miscarriage, and it is not recommended for persons of sanguine temperament.

**Rejuvenating facial mask**
Chop an apple in the blender and mix it with a little honey and finely chopped sage. Extend the paste over a freshly washed face and leave for fifteen minutes.

Vanilla is the fruit of a tropical orchid of Mexican origin. The Aztecs used it to flavour the chocolate drink that was customary after meals; this was *tlixochitl*, the name thay gave to vanilla. The vanilla plant is a parasite that uses its thick, exposed roots to climb trees 100 metres or more in search of sunlight. The yellow-green flowers open for just one day and there is a single, exclusively Mexican species of 'bee-bird' that pollinates them. Thanks to this tiny insect, Mexico was able to preserve her monopoly on vanilla exports for over 300 years, until the nineteenth century. Today it is also grown in Madagascar where it is artificially fertilized on plantations. The plant starts producing in its third year and continues for some fifty years. The flowers form long pods whose shape gave the plant its name (*vaina* means sheath in Spanish). The vanilla extract is obtained from the beans by fermenting in the sun; the beans are harvested just before they are fully ripe. In the fermentation process the colourless fruit acquires an exquisite, stimulating and exciting aroma that is appreciated for making pastry, liqueurs and perfumes. This fragrance is often replaced by synthetic vanilla, but the scent of true vanilla is inimitable because it is the result of a natural equilibrium between vanillin and other aromatic substances contained in the bean.

The effects of vanilla are numerous – tonic, stimulant, digestive and antiseptic – but it is hardly used in medicine. In the kitchen it has won a favoured place for itself in sweets. Who has never had the treat of enjoying vanilla custard, pudding, ice cream and cakes?

The name comes from the Greek word meaning valour. Medieval knights, when they needed courage before their tourneys, adorned themselves with a sprig of thyme. The Egyptians used it as a perfume and to embalm their dead, and ever since ancient times it has been appreciated for its culinary and medicinal qualities.

Thyme is native to the Mediterranean and abounds in the Latin countries, in dry, sunny places where its intense fragrance perfumes the atmosphere.

The flowered branches are harvested when they begin to bloom in spring, when their aroma is sharpest, and are dried in bunches hung from a thread in the shade. Because thyme is green all year long, it can always be used fresh.

The entire plant is usable. The young fresh sprouts are used in small amounts for seasoning salads and tomatoes, and the fresh or dried leaves are good with meat, roasts, fish, sauces and pizzas. Along with bay leaves and parsley, thyme is part of the traditional *bouquet garni* used by so many cooks.

Because of its wealth of curative qualities, an infusion of thyme is recommended for convalescence from illness and for anemia, tiredness, difficult digestion, worms, nervousness, whooping cough, rheumatism and gout. But taken in excess, more than two cups a day, it may prove toxic. Baths with thyme are pleasant, fortifying and stimulate blood circulation.

**Wine**
Leave 25g of dried flowers in 1 litre of dry white wine for fifteen days, then filter. A small glass after meals makes a good digestive.

Mustard was already known and used well before the Christian era. The Greeks called it *sinapi*, meaning harmful to the eyes, because of its strongly irritating action. In the New Testament the seed figures as a motif in one of Christ's parables: 'The kingdom of heaven is like a mustard seed . . .'

The plant came originally from the Orient and the Romans brought it to Europe where it grows wild along rocky paths and embellishes fields where crops are grown with its whitish-yellow flowers, although it is usually considered a weed.

The ripe fruit is harvested in summer when its yellow colour becomes ochre. The plants are beaten to remove the seeds, which are dried and ground and used to prepare one of our best-known condiments, mustard. It is used in small amounts to accompany meat and facilitates its digestion. The young fresh leaves make an appetizing addition to salads.

In natural medicine mustard is appreciated for the laxative effect of its seeds, taken whole, and is commonly used in poultices for treating rheumatism.

Black mustard is similar to the white variety, but its flavour and effects are stronger. It is not recommended for internal use because of its irritating action and the serious inflammations it can cause. Taken in excess, it may even be poisonous. The properties of black mustard are best utilized in the form of compresses, poultices or baths.

**Suggestion**
A pinch of black mustard powder placed inside your socks in the morning will keep your feet from being cold.

At least 2,000 years ago cooks and shamans in the Mediterranean countries used this aromatic plant, which is also called royal thyme. The Greeks, always fired by poetry and legend, thought it to be aphrodisiac and called it *satyres* in honour of those mythological creatures who used savory in their amorous feats. In the Middle Ages no love elixir mixed by witches was without savory, and the famous physician Mattioli warned about consuming too much of the plant because 'it spurs on the ardours of the body'.

There are two varieties found throughout Europe: garden savory and mountain savory. Both give off a pleasant fragrance and their flavour is bitter and pungent with a slight peppery taste. The leaves of wild savory are darker, narrower and brighter and its flavour more bitter. But the culinary and medicinal virtues of both varieties are essentially the same. The best time to harvest the plant is while it is blooming and just before.

Savory is an excellent seasoning for dried pulses and helps to prevent the gas caused by them. It can also be used – always in moderate amounts because of its strong flavour – with vegetables, goat cheese, fish and meat. The dried leaves, together with sage and thyme, give a delicious taste to stuffings; the fresh leaves are stronger and it is not advisable to cut or chop them as they will release abundant amounts of a bitter substance. Savory is also used in making liqueurs.

The medicinal virtues of savory are most effective in stimulating baths and infusions for stomach ailments, coughs, bronchitis and asthma. For persons on a salt-free diet savory – like tarragon – can be used as a substitute for salt and for pepper as well.

*Also published by Orbis Publishing Limited*

**The Encyclopedia of Herbs and Herbalism**
edited by Malcolm Stuart (available in hardback and paperback)

Depósito legal B. 9208-1985
Grafos S.A. 08013 Barcelona